Rhymes of Nature
Meet Me at the Salish Sea

Poetry by Nancy Oline Klimp

Illustrations by Jared Noury

Rhymes of Nature

Meet Me at the Salish Sea

Published by Nature Speaks To Us, LLC, Bainbridge Island, Washington.
Book design by Mi Ae Lipe (whatnowdesign.com).
Printed in the United States of America.

To contact the author or order additional copies:
NatureSpeaksToUs.com

First Edition, 2021
ISBN: 978-1-7351844-0-1
Library of Congress Control Number: 2020912433
Ebook ISBN-13: 978-1-7351844-1-8

MCP Books
2301 Lucien Way #415
Maitland, FL 32751
407.339.4217
www.millcitypress.net

To Dorothy, my mother,
who taught me to
"Notice nature patiently."

The Salish Sea

A miniature ocean
Constantly in motion

Tides running forth and back
Sometimes active, sometimes slack

Runoff waters from the land
Mountain snows to shoreline sand

An estuary system ancient, large, and productive
Its diverse ecology, highly instructive

The Salish Sea is an inland sea that extends from southwestern British Columbia in Canada to northwest Washington State in the United States.

Its intricate waterways, inlets, and bays include the Puget Sound, the cities of Seattle and Vancouver, BC, and 419 islands, including the San Juan Islands near the Canadian border.

It is one of the world's most biologically diverse inland seas, home to 37 species of mammals, 253 species of fish, 172 species of birds, and thousands of types of invertebrates. Over a hundred of these species are threatened and endangered, and many people and organizations are working to conserve and protect them.

Its name comes from the first inhabitants of the region, the Coast Salish. Although these indigenous peoples are ethnically related, they come from many different tribes that each have their own distinct cultures, languages, and customs.

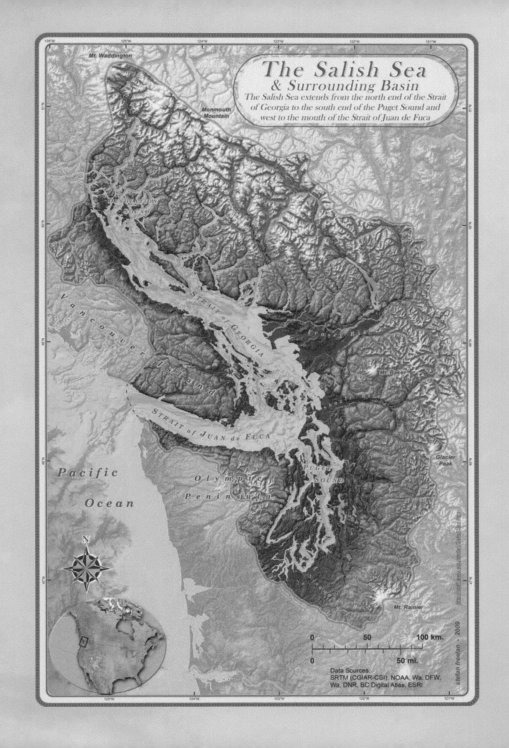

The Salish Sea
& Surrounding Basin
The Salish Sea extends from the north end of the Strait of Georgia to the south end of the Puget Sound and west to the mouth of the Strait of Juan de Fuca

Puget Sound

A fjord-like part of the Salish Sea
Underwater canyons form this estuary

Named for Peter, a sailor long ago
On his voyage of discovery, methodical and slow

Hundreds of meters down, a depth most deep
Where aquatic creatures swim, float, slither, and creep

This salty sea mingles with fresh water from the land
Back and forth in movement of rock, shell, and sand

Flooded glacial valleys carved out back in time
Follow nature's system of rhythm and rhyme

Canoes

Can you? Can you? Can you canoe?
Transport, centuries old, not all that new

Oars parting waters—forward, down, and through
Carved from a cedar tree, its longevity true

Carefully chosen and selected with respect
To voyage with an elegance so perfect

Created with pride by Native Americans in their own wise way
"The Paddle to Seattle" honored Washington State's 100th birthday!

Wings over Water, Wings over Land

Look skyward, gliding in the air
How, oh how, did they get up there?

From bald eagle to robin with feathers firm yet soft
The shape of their wings holds the key to staying aloft

The airflow lifts wings up high
Where they're free to soar, glide, and dive in the sky

Seasons

We have three
And one more, you see

They blend and bend in four shifts
Each in its variety, offering many gifts

Spring awakes, buds bursting
Summer bakes, earth warming

Fall drifts in, leaves floating
Winter chills, snow falling

Every season offers new celebrations
With nature's differences and contemplations

Trees Dance

Trees dance in the wind
On a Puget Sound summer day
Fir trees dancing in the wind
See them swing and sway

Trees dance in the wind
On a Puget Sound autumn day
Maple trees dancing in the wind
Won't their leaves be still and stay?

Trees dance in the wind
On a Puget Sound winter day
Birch trees dancing in the wind
What do their branches say?

Trees dance in the wind
On a Puget Sound spring day
Cedar trees dancing in the wind
See their forests in abundant array

Winds

Trade winds blow from east to west
Westerlies aim in reverse directions with zest

Sometimes blustery and full of blow
They shed mist, rain, and even snow

From the north, a chilly chill they can bring
From the south, a warm prelude to spring

Roots and Trunks

Mighty western hemlocks shelter rhododendron glens
In this Evergreen State where beauty never ends

Seedlings sprout into saplings
From water and light happenings

Deciduous trees shed their leaves
Evergreens hold on to their green sleeves

Spruce, pine, maple, larch, and yew—
To name from hundreds of species, just a few

To learn the secrets of their stage
Count their inner rings of age

When the tree decomposes and decays
Passing from its living days

It creates a soft forest bed
From fir and madrone to cedars cinnamon red

Mushrooms

So many kinds of caps on a stalk
You may have seen them on a walk

Lion's mane, matsutake, angel wings, and chanterelles
Lobster, oyster, porcini, bolete, and morels

They help our environment as they absorb and digest
Mushrooms and their bioremediation are the very best

They thrive with lots of water vapor in the air
They help our climate and grow everywhere

Over eight miles of mycelium in a cubic inch of soil
Of their contributions, there is no dispute to spoil

The largest living organism on the planet
Creates Earth's own natural internet

Nature's treasures—the ultimate hide-and-go-seek
After a rain, you can sneak a peek!

Owls

Some owls whistle and hoot
Others bark, shriek, and toot

Fearless hunters of the night
Known for their swift and silent flight

Necks that turn 270 degrees
As they roost in mature canopy trees

With excellent vision and acute hearing
The barn owl's heart-shaped face is endearing

Screech, pygmy, great-horned, and saw-whet—
In their ecosystem they all perfectly fit

Hummingbirds

These are the smallest birds around Puget Sound
For acrobatic flying, they're simply renowned

Like miniature helicopters, these little jewels hover
Darting forward, backward—long distances they cover

Just a few inches long—so small and compact
When flowers abound, to nectar they do attract

Hunger makes them seek orange and red
Their speeding metabolisms must be fed

Tiny, fearless, feisty, and aggressive
They fly distances and speeds impressive

Great Blue Herons

With a four-foot wingspan, they stand over a meter tall
Flying with deep wingbeats, uttering a croaking call

Slow, precise aerodynamics in flight
Legs trailing and necks tucked in tight

They hunt slowly with bodies slender and straight
Their S-shaped necks, a spring-action trait

With lightning-quick movements, they stalk their prey
These long-legged waders, camouflaged in blue-gray

Their plumage sleekly shines as they move with stealth
Their presence reveals our shoreline waters' health

They weave their nests with twigs high up in tall trees
Their colonies are called rookeries or heronries

Trumpeter Swans

As winter nears, they visit for a while
Snowy white with an elegant style

Of all the waterfowl, they're the heavyweight
Black webbed feet, necks graceful and straight

Whooping like a French horn
Of their presence they do warn

In spring and fall occur their migrations
Following their sky path with aerodynamic formations

Harbor Seals

A popular marine mammal in Puget Sound
Bodies gray, black, or brown-sleek and round

They can plunge down hundreds of feet
Such an agile, web-finned water athlete

Related to dogs, weasels, and bears
This seal's big brown eyes cast curious stares

Whiskers help them navigate and hunt
They're often seen lolling on many a waterfront

Basking in the sun, they "haul out" on rocks and sand
Spending half their lives in water and half on land

Under the Top

Under the top
Aquatic action moves nonstop

Starfish not in the sky
On tiny tube feet they walk by

Transparent and graceful jellyfish propel
Through shifting estuary currents or a tidal swell

Sea anemones slowly slide
Crabs skitter-scutter side to side

Scallops clap their shells forward jetting
Kelp forests sway with seahorses hiding

Ducks, swans, and geese paddle their feet
Underwater webbed strokes, strong and fleet

Herring, lingcod, perch, and sculpin
Guided along by gill, tail, and fin

We Are Orcas

We're massive marine mammals
Not related to fish but to camels!

Called the "Wolves of the Sea"
We live in groups cooperatively

Our lifelong pods are J, K, and L
Puget Sound is where we dwell

Echolocation guides us to our mealtime morsels
Speeding through the water assisted by our dorsals

We are magnificent, curious, smart sea creatures
Our matrilineal leaders guide these features

An intricate underwater language we speak
As important communication we seek

We leap, breach, and swim, with powerful fluke tails
Each move has meaning for us gentle giant whales

Octopus

Not a cat born in October
But a leggy creature living as a loner

Swimming close to Seattle's metropolis
Might sound quite preposterous

Named "the Giant Octopus of the Pacific"
Its intelligence is most terrific

Belonging to the phylum Mollusca so robust
The octopus is nocturnal, awakening at dusk

An invertebrate, no skeleton, so flexible
It has eight legs, each called a tentacle

Ferries

White with green trim all around
Skimming waters with minimal sound

They float on marine highways, like watery bridges
Many fathoms above underwater canyon ridges

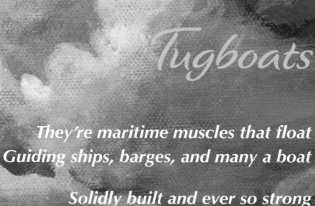

Tugboats

They're maritime muscles that float
Guiding ships, barges, and many a boat

Solidly built and ever so strong
Diesel engine power moves them along

Forward and backward they push, pull, and turn
Respect from others is easy to earn

Port 'n' starboard—strong 'n' stable
Tugboats are small vessels, yet ever so able

Tugboats work in weather of all sorts
Maneuvering aquatic craft precisely to their ports

Shimmering Puget Sound

Shimmering waters
Sparkle like diamonds
Glisten as gems
When sunlight shines overhead

Shimmering waters
Clouds paint colors
Translucent blues and greens
Some dark as the darkest lead

Shimmering waters
Raindrops fall and bounce
A vertical curtain comes down
Lakes, rivers, and ocean are fed

Shimmering waters
Phases of the moon
Reflecting and shining
Even as we rest in bed

Shimmering Puget Sound

Glossary

aerodynamic
Having a shape that reduces the drag from air moving past

aloft
At a great height

aquatic
Relating to living in or near water

bioremediation
Bacteria, fungi, or green plants working to break down contaminants into less harmful substances

breach
The rising and breaking through the surface of the water, as a whale does

camouflage
Something (color or shape) that protects an animal from danger by making it difficult to see in the area around it

canopy
The highest layer of branches in a forest or a tree colony

communication
The sharing or exchange of information, news, thoughts, feelings, and ideas via words, sounds, signs, and behaviors

conserve/conservation
To protect or the protection of an environmentally or culturally important place or thing from destruction

contemplation
Thinking about or looking at something for a long time

decay
To rot or decompose through the action of bacteria or fungus

deciduous
A tree or shrub that sheds its leaves every year

decompose
To slowly break down naturally

degree
A unit of measurement for angles or arcs of a circle; a full rotation is 360 degrees

diverse
Different in chemistry, form, and purpose

dorsal
A tall triangular fin on the back of a fish or whale, used for balance and stability

echolocation
The sonar system used by whales, dolphins, and bats to locate objects by reflected sound for navigating, hunting, and avoiding obstacles

ecology
The study of living things and their environments

ecosystem
Everything that exists within a complex community of living things (such as plants and animals) and their environmental function as a unit

estuary
An area where a river flows into the sea

evergreen
A plant that retains green leaves throughout the year

fathom
A nautical measurement used to determine the depth of water; one fathom equals six feet (1.83 meters)

feathers
The soft, lightweight covering that surrounds birds' outer bodies; beneath outer feathers are down feathers

fin
A flattened appendage on an aquatic animal (such as a fish or a whale), used to propelling, steering, and balance

fjord
A narrow inlet of the sea between steep slopes, typically formed by submerged glaciated valleys

fleet
Swift in motion

fluke
One of the halves of a whale's tail

gill
The body part that a fish uses to breathe

glacier/glacial
A very large area of ice that moves slowly down a slope or valley

glen
A secluded narrow valley

haul out
The act of leaving the ocean to spend time on land; seals "haul out" on rocks or beaches to regulate their body temperature, give birth, rest, and raise their pups

heronry/heronries
A place where herons breed and nest, usually in groups of trees

indigenous
Living or occurring natively in a particular region

invertebrate
A type of animal that has no backbone

jetting
A motion of travel through a narrow opening with great force, such as the way a jellyfish swims by contracting the muscles around its bell

lead
A heavy soft metal that has a gray color

mammal
A type of animal that is warm-blooded and feeds milk to its young; whales, humans, dogs, and cats are mammals

maneuvering
To move skillfully or carefully

marine
Relating to the sea or the plants and animals that live in the sea

maritime
Relating to sailing, navigating, or doing business by sea

matrilineal
Relating to descent or kinship through the maternal (female) line

meter
A unit of length measuring 39.37 inches

methodical
A planned and orderly way of doing something

metropolis
A very large or important city

migration
To move from one area to another at different times of the year

Mollusca
The phylum of invertebrate mollusks, such as octopus, snails, and clams

mycelium
The part of a fungus consisting of a network of fine white threads called hyphae

nectar
A sweet liquid produced by flowers

nocturnal
Active at night

phylum
A large group of related plants or animals

plumage
The feathers that cover a bird's body

Explore my forests, my marshlands
Climb my hills to seek a view
Walk my shoreline waters
My nature will delight you
For I am gentle and I am true

— Mother Nature —

pod
A group of ocean animals that swim together, such as whales

port (place)
A town or city where ships stop to load and unload cargo

port (direction)
The left side of a vessel looking forward

propel
To cause movement in a particular direction, usually forward

Puget Sound
An inlet of the Pacific Ocean that is part of the Salish Sea on the northwest coast of the United States in Washington State

raptor
A bird (such as an eagle or hawk) that hunts and eats other animals

rookery/rookeries
A place where a group of birds or social mammals (such as seals or penguins) breed, nest, or raise their young

runoff
Water from rain or snow that flows over the surface of the ground and ultimately into streams

Salish Sea
An inland sea that extends from southwestern British Columbia in Canada to northwest Washington State in the United States

scutter
To move fast with short, small steps

sea anemones
A group of flowery-looking marine predatory animals that stay attached to rocks under the sea

shimmering
To shine with a wavering vibrating light

skeleton
The framework or protecting structure of a living thing, internal or external

skitter
To skim, glide, or skip along a surface

starboard
The right side of a ship, looking forward

swell
To expand (as in size, volume, or numbers) gradually beyond a normal limit

tail
The rear part of an animal's body used for propulsion

tentacle
Long, flexible structures that extend from the head or mouth of an animal (such as an octopus, jellyfish, or anemone), used for feeling and grasping

translucent
Allows light to pass through so objects behind can be seen but not in details

tribe
A social group made up of many families, clans, or generations that share the same language, customs, and beliefs

waterfowl
A large bird that is found in or near water (such as a goose or duck)

westerlies
Winds blowing from the west

wingspan
The distance between the tips of a pair of wings (such as on a bird or an airplane)

Nature is the source of all true knowledge. She has her own logic, her own laws. She has no effect without cause nor invention without necessity.

— Leonardo da Vinci —

Educational Notes

Salish Sea

See the Salish Sea section at the beginning of this book.

Salish Sea Marine Sanctuary | salishsea.org

Wikipedia | en.wikipedia.org/wiki/Salish_Sea

Puget Sound

The Puget Sound is an inlet of the Pacific Ocean and part of the Salish Sea in the coastal region of the Pacific Northwest in the American state of Washington, west of the Cascade mountain range and east of the Olympic Mountains. The term sometimes also refers to the Puget Sound region, which includes the Washington State cities of Seattle, Tacoma, Olympia, and Everett. Puget Sound is also the third-largest estuary in the United States.

The SeaDoc Society | seadocsociety.org

Encyclopedia of Puget Sound | eopugetsound.org

Canoes

The canoes of the Native Americans of the Salish Sea region are built for its sheltered waters and are renowned for their size, speed, and grace. They have long been used for fishing, hunting, and trade. A canoe is usually carved from a single log of red cedar. When a tree is chosen, a prayer is offered to thank the tree for its sacrifice. Once a canoe is launched, a dedication and naming ceremony is held to recognize its carvers. Tribal Journeys is an annual event hosted by different indigenous tribes in Alaska, British Columbia, and Washington State, where families travel by canoe to visit the hosting nations to celebrate.

Tribal Journeys | tribaljourneys.wordpress.com

Don's Maps | donsmaps.com/canoesnwc.html

Wings over Water, Wings over Land

Whether they belong to birds or planes, wings are especially shaped to help air flow over and under them. When birds flap their wings, the force created is called thrust. How air moves over and under a wing is different; the higher pressure beneath a wing creates lift, which enables a bird to lift off the ground.

Ask a Biologist, Arizona State University | askabiologist.asu.edu/how-do-birds-fly

Seasons

Seasons occur because the tilt of the Earth's axis changes over the course of a year. In the Northern Hemisphere, the Earth leans toward the sun in the summer and away from it in the winter. The autumn and spring equinoxes are both midpoints. In the Northern Hemisphere, spring runs from March through May; summer is June through August; autumn is September through November; and winter is December though February.

National Aeronautics and Space Administration (NASA) | spaceplace.nasa.gov/seasons/en

Trees Dance

The Pacific Northwest is full of trees! Maples have large leaves that are colorful in the fall; their seeds are little "helicopters" with "wings" that help them to spiral to the ground. Firs grow very large and can live 500 to 1,000 years; their thick bark helps them survive forest fires. Cedars are some of the biggest, most common evergreen trees in the Pacific Northwest. Birches are deciduous trees, meaning that they lose their leaves every fall; their thin white bark often peels off in layers.

Environmental Systems Research Institute (ESRI) | arcgis.com/apps/MapJournal/index. html?appid=d3295191730a49f691379d7962b20bb0

The Nature Conservancy | washingtonnature.org/cities/trees

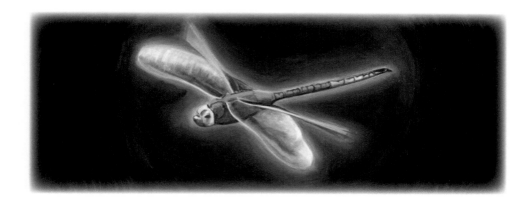

In every walk with nature, one receives far more than one seeks.

— John Muir —

Winds

The diverse topography around the Salish Sea affects its wind and weather patterns. Convergence zones form when large marine airflows split around the Olympic Mountains and converge over the Puget Sound, causing strong storms, rain, hail, or snow.

Cliff Mass | cliffmass.blogspot.com

Wikipedia | en.wikipedia.org/wiki/Puget_Sound_Convergence_Zone

Roots and Trunks

Trees have three major organs: roots, stems, and leaves. A tree's roots absorb water and nutrients from the soil, store sugar, and anchor the tree upright in the ground. The trunk (stem) supports the crown, giving the tree its shape and strength. The leaves produce food for the tree; together, the leaves and branches at the top of the tree form its crown.

Pacific Northwest Chapter of the International Society of Arboriculture | pnwisa.org/page/how-trees-grow

Mushrooms

Over 1,500 different mushrooms live in the Pacific Northwest, many of them in its lush forests. Mushrooms are not plants but unique organisms called fungi that are vital to the health of trees and the environment. They are made up of more than 90 percent water and do not require sunlight. Some of them are good to eat (edible) while others are poisonous. Some even glow in the dark!

Puget Sound Mycological Society | psms.org

Daniel Winkler | mushroaming.com/Pacific_Northwest

Owls

Owls are nocturnal raptors with hooked bills and needle-sharp talons (claws). Their lightweight bodies and wide wings allow them to swoop down on their prey without making noise. Their vision and hearing are excellent, and their colors and patterns help them blend into their environment (camouflage).

Seattle Audubon Society | seattleaudubon.org/sas/Learn/SeasonalFacts/Owls.aspx

Hummingbirds

Hummingbirds are the smallest of all birds. Four species live in the Puget Sound region; rufous, calliope, black-chinned, and Anna's. Hummingbirds are pollinators, meaning that they carry pollen from one flower to another. They have fast metabolisms, eating up to 50 percent of their body weight each day. About 30 percent of their weight comes from their flight muscles.

Avianweb, Beauty of Birds | beautyofbirds.com/hummingbirdswashingtonstate.html

BirdWeb, Seattle Audubon Society | birdweb.org/birdweb

Great Blue Herons

In 2003, the great blue heron was named Seattle's official city bird. These hunters live in freshwater marshes, rivers, and lakes and saltwater mudflats and shores. These powerful predators can swallow a fish many times wider than its narrow neck. They fly on average about 25 to 35 miles per hour.

Slater Museum | pugetsound.edu/academics/academic-resources/slater-museum/exhibits/marine-panel/great-blue-heron/

Seattle Audubon Society | seattleaudubon.org/sas/learn greatblueheron/facts.aspx

Trumpeter Swans

More trumpeter swans live in Washington State than anywhere else in the contiguous United States. Named for their unusual call, they migrate from Alaska or Canada and stay in Puget Sound from November to April. They are the heaviest bird in North America, with a wingspan of over ten feet. Their long necks allow them to forage for submerged plants without diving.

The Trumpeter Swan Society | trumpeterswansociety.org

Northwest Swan Conservation Association | nwswans.org

Harbor Seals

Harbor seals are the most common year-round resident marine mammal in the Salish Sea. You may see them floating in the water or surfacing to breathe. Their large eyes and sensitive whiskers help them see, navigate safely, and hunt for fish in the deep, dark water. Their spotted coats come in a variety of colors, from white or silver gray to black and dark brown. They take naps in the water or sometimes come ashore to sleep.

Seattle Aquarium | seattleaquarium.org/animals/harbor-seals

The SeaDoc Society | seadocsociety.org/harbor-seal-facts

We Are Orcas

Orcas (sometimes called killer whales) are among the most iconic and beloved symbols of the Salish Sea. These largest members of the dolphin family are very social and live in extended-family groups called pods. The three pods (J, K, and L) that live year-round in the Salish Sea are collectively called the Southern Resident Killer Whales. Each orca can be identified by the unique shape of its dorsal fin. These skilled hunters feed mostly on salmon but their food supply is threatened by climate change and human impacts on the environment. Many organizations are working to help the orcas.

Center for Whale Research | whaleresearch.com

Orca Network | orcanetwork.org

The Whale Museum | whalemuseum.org

Octopus

The octopus is a soft-bodied mollusk with eight limbs called tentacles. The Puget Sound is home to the world's largest octopus, the giant Pacific octopus. These remarkable creatures are invertebrates, meaning that they have no bones. They are very intelligent and their eyes are very well developed—they can even remember and recognize human faces! The largest-known specimen weighed 600 pounds and had an arm span of about 30 feet. They can also change color depending on their mood.

Seattle Aquarium | seattleaquarium.org/animals/giant-pacific-octopus

Ferries

Today's distinctive white and green ferryboats have grown from the original "mosquito fleet" of boats in the early 1900s that served Seattle and Puget Sound's many islands. Carrying nearly 25 million passengers annually, Washington State Ferries (WSF) is the largest ferry system in the United States and the fourth largest in the world. Each ferry can carry up to 200 vehicles and 2,500 passengers. Most ferry names come from Native American tribes and refer to a tribal group or local nature. Some examples are Sealth (Suquamish/Duwamish, for Chief Seattle), Tacoma (Southern Lushootseed: "snowy mountain"), Elwha (Chinook dialect: "elk"), Samish (Samish: "giving people"), and Cathlamet (Kathlamet: "stone").

Washington Department of Transportation | wsdot.wa.gov/ferries/terminals/our-fleet

Tugboats

Equipped with powerful engines that push and pull, tugboats help move large or disabled vessels in crowded harbors or narrow channels, either by direct contact or with a tow line. The first Puget Sound tugboats began operating in the mid-1800s as part of the logging industry. Steam engines powered early tugboats but today most are diesel. Tugboat captains must consider many factors: the weight of the ship they are guiding, tides, winds, waves, and other boats. A Norweigian immigrant woman named Thea Foss started a rowboat rental company in Tacoma in 1889, which later became Foss Maritime, one of the largest tugboat companies in the Pacific Northwest. Its distinctive green-and-white tugs still operate in Seattle and Tacoma today.

Wikipedia | wikipedia.org/wiki/Seattle_tugboats

Foss Maritime Company | foss.com

Tugboat Information | tugboatinformation.com

Acknowledgments

The author and illustrator wish to thank the following people and entities who granted permission to use their photography and map as references and artistic sources.

River Otters — Nicole Duplaix (photographer)

Salmon — Jonny Armstrong (photographer)

Salish Sea — *Map of the Salish Sea and Surrounding Basin,* Stefan Freelan (cartographer), Western Washington University, 2009

Wings over Water — Glenn Sadowski (photographer)

Roots & Trunks — Black-tailed deer by Tom and Pat Leeson (photographers), leesonphoto.com

Owls — Derivative of *"Bubo virginianus (Grand-duc d'Amérique).jpg"* by Mary C. Kirby (photographer), licensed under CC BY 2.0

Derivative of "Barred Owl Flying Down #3" by Eleanor Kee Wellman (photographer)

Hummingbirds — Photographers Mark Turner (wildflowers) and Terry Birch (hummingbirds)

Trumpeter Swans — Derivative of "Trumpeter Swan" by Karl Heil (photographer), US Fish and Wildlife Service, public domain

Harbor Seals — Mark Dodge (photographer)

Shimmering Puget Sound — Derivative of "Coast Salish Fish Trap" by Richard Eriksson (photographer), licensed under CC BY 2.0

I deeply appreciate the knowledgeable encouragement of Mi Ae Lipe, John Klimp, Florrie Munat, Hilda Weins, Alice Acheson, Karen Noury, Paul Heys, Tia Rich, John DesCamp, Karen Nelson, Pam Christensen, and Ben Schill. They have all proven invaluable on this "Meet Me Journey of Exploration."

Jared Noury's artistry has brought vibrant life to these poems.

Thank you, everyone!

—Nancy Oline Klimp